No Name

To be a Witch is Not a Willed Thing

No Name

To be a Witch is Not a Willed Thing

A Psychological Tale
by
Guislaine Vincent de Damas

Illustrated by Consuelo Child-Villiers

First published in 2019
by DAMAS
Worlds End Studios
132 Lots Road
London SW10 0RJ

A CIP catalogue record for this book is available from The British Library

Guislaine Vincent de Damas, *No Name: To be a Witch is Not a Willed Thing*
First published in Great Britain in 2019.
© Guislaine Vincent de Damas, 2019.

Watercolour illustrations, 'Blue' oil painting on page 14 and unnumbered blue
pages throughout, and oil portrait of Guislaine Vincent de Damas,
are all © Consuelo Child-Villiers.

ISBN 978-1-9163199-9-8 Hardback

Keith Douglas, 'the seafloor of an afternoon' from his poem *Behaviour of Fish in
an Egyptian Tea Garden* (p.1). Lines (partly paraphrased) from Elizabeth Bishop's
poem *One Art* (p.40)

Design and production by Lucy Llewellyn at Head & Heart Book Design.

Printed in Great Britain by Blissetts of Acton.

To that which has no name

love and sorrow

CONTENTS

No Name

To be a Witch is Not a Willed Thing

Once upon a time on the seafloor of an afternoon when the rivers ran wild and the oceans were full of fish, a time between cities and countries, there was a King and a Queen, at home in their castle, high up on a hill. They had one daughter, a girl who was six years old. Times were good, or so they said. So long as the witch down the road let it be. But the truth is...

...that such all–too-easy times were getting on the witch's nerves. She was more than restless. She'd lost her broom, and this left her hard on the ground.

'Why, when things go on pretending too well for too long it isn't good', the witch mumbled, passing by the twelve toads meditating on her doorstep. She brushed off, with the tip of her red lizard-skin shoe...

...a tidy pile of dead flies. She clapped her hands at the skies, and the clouds, replying with a burst of heavy rain, lowered themselves. Lower and lower, their woolly and ghostly forms solidified whereupon, reaching the ground, they turned into an army of men in suits of steel with helmets of shiny black plastic and dark glasses made of mirrors. They trooped across the mountains and across the plains, crushing in their path weeds and roses all; and there was war.

'That's better', the witch said to her denizens. 'Now King and Queen will wail and weep and have a breakdown and then things will change. Why, K & Q, always so terribly busy and hurried, hadn't taken the time to give their daughter a name. Soon as they'd felt the ground tremble under their velvet slippers, announcing thundering armies, they had taken off in the royal ship and disappeared over the horizon quicker than smoke, forgetting, in their rude hurry, their unnamed child.

A sickly atmosphere, manifesting itself in a mustardy yellow colour, wafted throughout the castle, making its ancient walls ooze and sweat. She without name, barely able to breathe in the poisoned air, gathered her necessities, and left the castle. There were no thoughts in her head. No need for thought when you have limbs that know how to do and where to go. She had a lamp – magic because it provided its own light when touched in a certain manner – and a book. The lamp cast a glow, encircling her in gentle, pale-as-moonlight warmth. The book, made of pictures and letters – some of which gathered themselves into the making of a word or two, depending on how you looked at them – informed her of many things, things about life which people couldn't or wouldn't speak of.

In the woods to which she was heading there lived, and had lived for a very long time in fairy tale time, give or take a century, a young-ish bear. His name was Mishka. When he saw No Name trotting along inside a circle of a mysterious pale light, he followed.

After a while, as day slipped away in its usual invisible way, and night took its place, No Name put her book down, rested her small head, empty of words, but full of everything else, and soon fell into good sleep – something she did well, trusting the falling. The secret is to let go, drop down to where there is no bottom, to where you just float on the ocean of sweet, sculpted air.

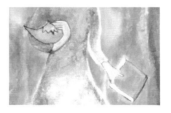

Mishka the bear, really a prince from centuries past, had been cast into a spell by the eternally restless, witchy flux of his own nature. It was in this moment out of time that he understood two things. One, that there is no justice in the forest. Two, that Chance happens. He was being brought, if not sent, a friend. A she-friend no less, who might even help turn him back into the human being he once almost was but for his rather rough, if not to say unevolved, uncivilised, manner. Although he had no idea how such transformation might take place, he thought for a start to take back to his den she who was nameless. And wait. And see. None of this was to do with kindness, it was just that the bear sensed there was something in it for him which he badly needed, even if he didn't know what that was, yet. He did give thought to how he might turn into the Prince he truly was meant to be. And even that it was up to him to reach through a misty memory, past the bitter root of existence, to some curse laid down upon him – or inherited from his animal ancestry – so very long ago.

In this way, the bear knew his bewitched animal side could be set free, no doubt at some cost to his pride which, if willingly broken down, might then allow him to emerge into personhood. By instinct, he also knew that the curse would lift only if a child without name sang him a song true to the sorrows of bone and flesh. This was conditional, of course, as most of life is, on the child singing from the heart in the way of that small bird, the wren, its tiny chest quivering with a lion-hearted songsound.

What Mishka did not know is that the little girl, in her fright, had left her voice   behind, somewhere up in the castle on the hill, along with sensations   yet to sound themselves into language.

Time, in such spaces as cities and countries, has a way of flying past, and before you know it you are a hundred and one years old, and it's too late to wake up. But this child without name did wake up, if some years later, when the war that changed everything was over (just for now). Things were trying to grow again. The king and queen had returned, old and tired and sad, their hearts arid without a child to whom they might bequeath the sweet and sour of their kingdomcome. Why they'd even lost their capital letters to lower case. The stars they had once been in the firmament of No Name's sky had lost their shine, as stars do when night gives way to the truth of a day without love and care.

As night and day passed through the forest, trees listening and bending respectfully to the winds of change, there came to be, against the odds, a single young rose. Though growing in the deep shade of her forest-home made her a little leggy, the effort of it taught the rose how to stretch beyond her reach for those brief (so precious), slanted moments of sun rays.

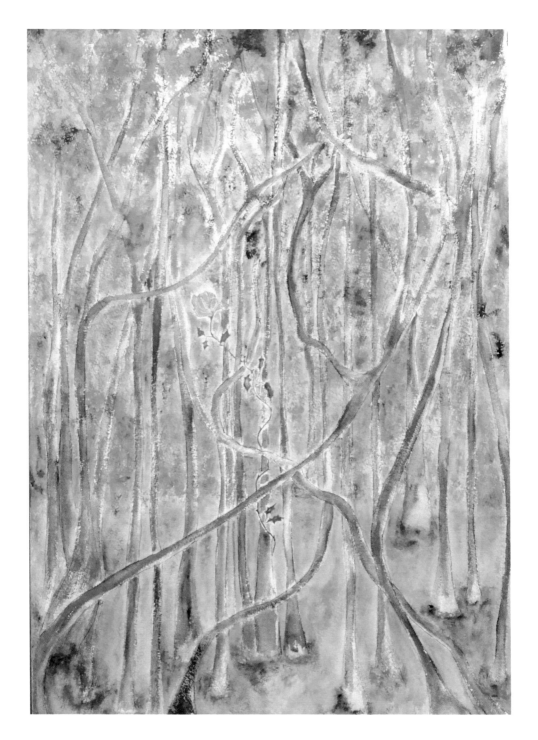

No Name was turning into a lovely young woman and, though still not yet named, she was about to be the bride of the bear she had taken shelter with – or perhaps had been abducted by – she could never quite know nor, of course, say.

But time spent with Mishka the bear, listening to his thoughts and wishes and the way he shared his (many) views on life, made her fond of him, and curious about the world he spoke of. While thoughts of her own, of the heart-centred kind, were rising up in her, she could feel their different shapes and sizes jostling for space.

And so there was this nagging problem of finding the precious words that held the key to the closed heart of the woman-child without name. The much-needed words were fast asleep inside the book under the lamp, still not yet ready to slip off the pages and up into her sky-mind, like little fishes coming up for air. It was as if the words knew that the descent to the underworld is not so rare. The wisdom is that it may even be a necessity. The true struggle lies in the retracing of steps, the climb back to the upper air; there the labour lies.

Animals being more patient than men, Mishka as bear was quite content to remain a bear, gathering honey, rolling up the lazy bones inside his fur coat, remaining in the embrace of the cave during the long cold winters. On the other hand, the princely self within was less contented and, if truth be known, the silence of the very slow-to-open rosebud was getting on his nerves. The witch was needed to stir things up again. After all, Mishka-bear did rather enjoy good conversation and was lonely without it, more and more fantasizing about the rose-girl's name, wanting to ask 'Come here'. But, 'come here' who?

The much-needed words tucked away inside the book, detached from whatever sentence they might once have belonged to, were words that appeared to be positioned on top of towers, all drawn in different heights. The first letter of each word stood up high, such as Voice, and Love. And then in a sort of cluster, a city skyline with the words Fish, Bird, Forest, Bear. A few pages later, all by itself, sitting on top of the highest tower of all, in a scribble, almost invisible, as if to remain silent – the word Sing.

Now the witch, when at home, suffering ennui, and more than a little morose for being a witch without a broom, sat on her chair made of bone and gristle and seashells and bendy willow branches – these last brought in by Mishka who was learning to befriend the forest witcheryness. She wore a long robe made of thick linen the colour of moody sky with scudding clouds, on the left breast was embroidered a large red strawberry with a tuft of green at the top. At her feet sat a grey cat, twitching its striped black and white tail, and beside the cat there lay one large, not-quite-smiling fish, gasping for air. Oh, it prayed, for just one drop of its mother ocean.

You may not know that to be a witch is not a willed thing. When it happens to you, it hurts, a lot. Pain travels through people for centuries and nobody listens to what it says to them until the witch, her nature exhausted, lets go and weeps. Pain is her proof of life.

One full tear, the size of a pebble, rolled down the witch's hollow cheeks. The fish swallowed this one saline drop of life, shaped as the letter O, with true gratitude. 'One more, please', asked the fish. It was then that, out of its O–shaped mouth, rolled a ring, rolling all the way to the bear's den. And there, inscribed in the ring, was a name.

Mishka could propose.

In parenthesis: How was it that in this unexpected, still-as-night moment, the witch's broom had materialised? *What could this have to do with love*, she wondered, deciding to treasure the thought to herself.

When the young rose of a girl heard the sound of her existence – a name ! – her heart broke into a thousand and one pieces. Love and sorrow. Love and sorrow. Love and sorrow.

It was like the sea, a big wave rising and spilling out of her eyes, typhooning, whirlpooling, the wheeling the tumble the up-the-staircase roaring through her eerie shells.

The time had come.

Sing!

With each song note the bear raised himself up and then, in the stillness of that moment, animal skin and rawhide and coarseness of fur slipped away, revealing the splendour of him, and of his soul.

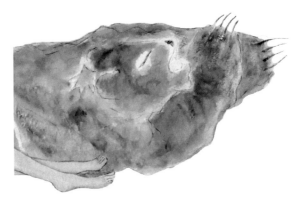

Half entailed
she rolls out
of the wave of his thought

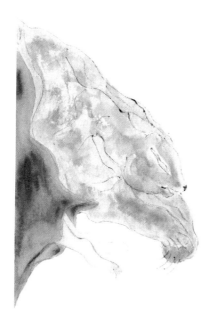

and then the curl, her hair
is foam, is wave, the crest, the spume
a wave, she is the wave

and like a mermaid she rides

the waves the swirl
and up the seashell's spiral stair

she lifts, she rises
whirlpool typhooning
across the sea
to land

a mermaid tossed onto the sand
as if a rose in his hand

"Oh, Mishka," she said.

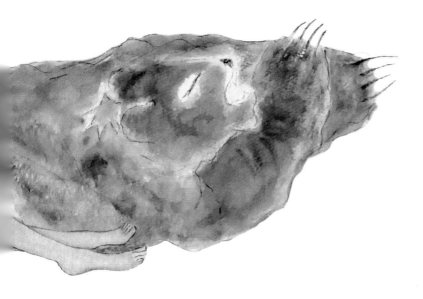

A PERSONAL AFTERWORD

HOW THE FABLE CAME TO BE

This little book has much to say. It is not easy for me to find the words. There are two stories. One is the fable – which entered my life as a fairy tale. The other is how the fable came to be – much more difficult to tell. It changes each time I try. Sometimes it seems not to want to be told. There is a portion of the sacred and private within the source of a story, a painting, a song, and passion. In this way, it will be incomplete, but my wish is for the fable to enchant and entice you as it did me.

*

About some seventeen years ago, a three-day workshop was being held on the *Word Association Experiment* which, as devised by C. G. Jung in 1907, was to reveal who or what was really doing the driving in our lives.

I need to keep this simple. We have complexes, or 'complexes have us', Jung would say. They are energies happening within, independently of our will. Bewitching, they have authority, they are autonomous. We'd better get to know them, find ways of getting on with them. I was invited to attend the workshop, along with other applicants training to become analytical psychotherapists (i.e., Jungian analysts who work with dreams and images).

Jung was adamant in saying that 'psyche is image'. This did not mean image as 'picture'. Image as movement in and out of form, shape, texture, feeling-tone, size, colour, sounds. This fascinated me, and I felt it would take my lifetime to think about what it meant, or understand at least a little – which would be more than enough; the territory has its dangers. Jung added to this dictum that image carried the feeling and the action. Now that was even more interesting to me. Intuitively I got it, but that was not enough. It had to be lived, the understanding coming from experience.

For instance, a fairy tale is not about the people in the tale – nor about its creatures, objects, landscape and buildings. *Cinderella* is not about a woman named Cinderella. It is about existence denied. There are moments when you might feel like Cinderella, but you are not her. Though you are feeling diminished, as if sweeping up the ashes of your life for no good purpose. The figure of Cinderella is an image pointing towards a feeling – not a sign, but a symbol, a thing charged with an energy leading the way to the unknown. But, sensed as 'true', you have to go with it. Ever since I was a child I imagined myself as an artist, like my mother. Psychology was the last thing on my mind. (Though there was a grandfather, Elton Mayo, on my mother's side, a distinguished eccentric gentleman, known in the 1920's as industrial psychologist, who died too soon, leaving, you could say, 'unfinished business' to fall on one of his grandchildren.)

Jung was ahead of the neuroscientists who today prove with their own instruments that 'thought is image'. The butterfly 'thinks' its geography across the world. I like to imagine it sees feelingly its way across vast distances. While my human brain, it seems, takes years to make verbal thought-sense of the strange sensations creeping up from behind it, like children playing grandmother's footsteps, and I continue to be fascinated by the inseparability of word and image.

At a point of deep crisis in Jung's life, lasting some anguished years, he said that he finally appealed to his hands, and began to carve wood. He wrote that this was his confession, finding expression of faith in stone, painting, sculpting, and building.

It is the profound satisfaction that goes into the making of things that can turn into an art and a way of living, of regenerating, of healing, putting Humpty Dumpty back together, some part of longed-for soul, and its broken spirit. Jung detected how change happens in the imagination before it shows

in a life, and the shape-shifting evolution of an image as it recurs in a life.

On the first day of the workshop we explored Jung's ideas. Our workshop and seminar leader explained the specifics of the Experiment we were about to apply to each other. Without complexes we lie still as stones, bored and boring, he said. These energies, once known as gods, have lost their names. Instead, we call them complexes. And there's no life in that. Jung had engraved on the lintel of the doorway of his home in Küsnacht, *Vocatus atque non vocatus Deus aderit*. In translation so much feeling is lost. Best said in a whisper that this Latin phrase stands for whether we believe or not believe, (the presence of) God is there. The archetype.

We are not truly masters in our own house until the ego learns that it is not king and queen of the realm. Instead, it is there to serve, and to relate to what Jung called the 'Self'. And by 'Self' Jung meant the organising principle of the whole personality. But what does that mean in the moment of your everyday?

We were to observe, when reading out the prescribed one hundred words to each other, signs such as hesitations, reverberations, stutterings, sighs, sweating, blushing, repetition. The depressive personality would, for instance, take longer to associate to a word. The manic would respond with 'clang' – nonsensical rhyming just for the hell of it, no interest in meaning. Jung was less interested in diagnosis, more in healing, what it is that heals. Numinosum. There can be no change or transformation without emotion.

In other words, the suffering of ourselves.

On the second day we were to choose a partner and, using a large sheet of graph paper and a chronometer, write down the number of seconds taken to respond to each called-out word. The words were all sorts, from abstract to figurative, from mother and father to house to sky, birds and objects, elements of water, air, fire, earth, and colours. Squares on the graph paper were filled, rising into towers going across the page from left to right. By the end, my psyche had drawn its own Manhattan skyline, as I saw it. We were to apply the Experiment to each other twice. Each session took roughly two hours. It was eerie to experience one's own hesitations, prolonged blanknesses, and laggings, all happening at exactly the same words.

Jung established the one hundred words, listing them in the order of noun, adjective, noun, verb. Neutral or weak words were woven and interlaced to allow the pulse to regain its comfortable rhythm after words that may have disturbed it. We were to start the stopwatch with the stimulus word and stop at the response however many seconds later. Though after ten or more seconds, we were to go on to the next word without comment.

We were told to always refer to this as Experiment and not Test. It has nothing to do with intelligence. There are no right or wrong answers. We were never to do the Experiment with people we didn't know or with close family members, or with any person with whom there might be a power relationship. And only with a person who had been thrown in the tumble dryer and experienced at least forty hours of Jungian analysis.

On the third day, our seminar leader said, 'Okay, now you write a fairy tale using as many of your skyscraper words' (i.e., your complex indicator words). We were to start with four drawings, and our tale was to begin with the words 'Once upon a time'. There was to be a heroine, and a hero. An introduction with statement of the problem. The ups and downs, peripeteia. A climax. A lysis. The tale was not to exceed three pages.

Complexes are the actors in our dreams. We need them, and they need their roles. And us. 'Find your myth', Jung would say. We thought to detect the presence of our complexes in the guise of objects and animals and human figures, how each stood in the way of creative endeavour, blocking the stream of life, causing havoc in our relationships, or not – perhaps, as well, guiding us towards what Jung called the Self and individuation. The form – architecture and rhythm – of the tale might hint at what was needed to dispel a curse, recognise the witch, good or bad, as being our 'attitude' to life. Ask 'how did I get here, how did what has happened, happen, and what has my role in this been'? Jung would say either you go screaming to the slaughter, or you go in your own way, eyes open.

*

Many years passed. I forgot about the fairy tale. Though I often wondered about my top skyscraper word. A verb, so simple. But my mind would not dance with it. My practice evolved. I worked in French, a language in which I am more confident. This contradicted my English self which tends to be less direct, and even more complex. I react to myself in French and Spanish and a linguistic mishmash from a childhood where I was brought up by aunts and grandmothers, laughing and crying and whispering about men and war in a macaronic language made of Russian, Brazilian, English, French, Spanish, German. Intellect, spirit, education of my thought, developed in English alongside my training as a psychotherapist in London. I play better in French.

A midlife crisis of my own happened, lasting years. Then tragedy. I was brought a book about the affair between Psyche and Eros resulting in a child they named Pleasure. Only a little book, and yet it performed the impossible, reaching far down and pulling me up back into the light. My life changed from being one way to being a different way – opposite, completely opposite. While (almost) everything I had known, and loved, was gone. Is this what Jung meant by find your myth? There was a pattern. Suspicious. I detected *le fil rouge* my grandmother and aunts talked about. Taking it personally, risking victimhood, I would be at its mercy. Taking hold of the reins and riding the pattern could make the difference between permanent residence in hell and climbing back up (with stupendous effort) into the upper air.

One day, an urge to write returned. I came across notes and forgotten journals and unfinished stories. And something I didn't recognise. A fairy tale written some fifteen years ago. I read it out loud to myself, instantly filled with goosefleshy delight. The secret alchemy of literature was happening. An architecture of image and sound stood in the silence of a sentence. I remembered from somewhere there must be chaos inside you to give birth to a dancing star. Now my top skyscraper complex word made sense. The universe having its way in love making. I read the tale again and again, out loud. Stopping mid-sentence whenever a nudge came to write a little more. A voice not my own turned the fairy tale into fable. The voice telling the tale enchanted me. Each time reading, in the same place, just as in the *Word Association Experiment*, a poem came to mind. 'The art of losing is not hard to master', it started. Down a few lines it said that a mother's watch, her door keys – the poet's, and a realm were lost: two cities, two rivers. At those last words I wept tears clean as rain. The poem ended remarking that 'the art of losing's not too hard to master/though it may look like (write it!) like disaster'.

I entered the imaging that my top complex words evoked in me, writing down what I saw as I felt it. Psyche is image. I curled up inside the feeling. Image carries the action. And it was while feeling the feeling, that figures and objects and events floated by between the lines as I read them.

It took me a while to notice that the fairy tale wasn't finished. After some weeks of reading it out loud (always at night), stopping here and there, learning to wait for an image to come through the pause. Or not. I would return to it on another day; I dreamed and woke up with thought of the tale; I took it out for a walk like the faithful canine trotting alongside down the street on our daily errands; I listened to a client speaking as if they had read the tale. Finally, after yet more weeks, the ending. But although I knew it was the end – there was that sense of recognition, for now at least – I didn't understand it. And then, I did.

ACKNOWLEDGEMENTS

To Consuelo Child-Villiers, something more than an acknowledgement.

It is about the exchange going on between Consuelo as artist and friend, and myself. I bought four of Consuelo's paintings soon after we first met. Maybe twelve years ago. I was in awe and in love with her images, her way of seeing, her paintings, her way with animals – on the canvas, and in life – and the way animal bodies in her paintings were strangely elongated, the way this reflected the arc of emotion traversing a body. One day, she asked if I would write two introductions to her work, one for a catalogue, one for a book – a retrospective of more than twenty-five years of painting. This thrilled and terrified me. I had never written about art. I accepted on the condition I could title my words as 'Not An Introduction'. It took months. I almost gave up. Especially the second time, for an exhibition entitled *Mythical Beasts*...

"...Enter the labyrinth where Consuelo Child-Villiers' 'Mythical Beasts and The Lion King' dwell, where the magic nature of things is the Real. Consider that Myth is a movement of the soul, in the form of Shahrázád in 'Figure with Serpent', a bejewelled reptilian encircling and intertwining its own story, and note the index finger so lightly taking hold of the serpent's tail ... The vital thing – a flash, a movement – best perceived from the corner of the eye, happens in Consuelo Child-Villiers' paintings ... let's say you look and look again, – at 'Unicorn'. You will see that her work is both abstract (background), and referential (form), that it is ardent in its expression of the artist's love-of-the-thing that cannot be seen and yet is there ... Matisse considered colours as forces which, in relationship, transformed ... And there is 'Blue' – whorls of

energy in an atomic dance of colour, layers upon layers of Woad Blue … traces of Bone Black, an abstraction of infinity, a breaking down and breaking through … from which a ghostliness of two forms holding hands evokes a still point in the midst of a vast swirling cosmos … And there is 'Red' – the unbounded explosive instability of matter reflecting back the volatile substance of emotion … an echoing Madder Red darkness where a dawning of light comes through from behind evoking the lesson learned in the dark – 'One must still have chaos in oneself to be able to give birth to a dancing star" – the word 'still' points to the creative process central to the artist, to the inside turned outwards, to the harnessing of a force, to the making of the Being with the One Horn … It is Nabokov who said the pattern of a thing precedes the thing. What would we do without this 'thing' or even the word itself…"

Working in this way, accepting Consuelo's challenge to write about her work, brought out my love of art, the mystery of it, and healed a part of my own conflicted relationship to art, reflecting eerily that with my artist mother. A rare kind of collaboration was going on. The gift went both ways.

More recently, I commissioned two portraits (one for each grandchild). The first was painted four years ago. Consuelo is right-handed. Then, that summer there was a terrible accident. Consuelo lost the use of her right hand for almost a year. I suggested (rather strongly) that she bring to life her left hand. She did. At first there were sketches in a shaky pencilling, then – impossible, extraordinary! – oils, then the second portrait of myself took hold. And so I own a right-handed portrait, and a left-handed portrait [see 'About the Author']. A remarkable event in itself. I was born left-handed as were my mother, sister, and my eldest daughter. I was made to switch to using my right hand, against creative self. These two portraits have put to bed the prejudice. And so now to this acknowledgement, the illustrations for the fable to which Consuelo has given her time – months – and imagination, enabling me to work and write with love. The entire 'Fable' project turns out to be about healing, complete with mystery.

1 Nietzsche, *Thus Spake Zarathustra*

To Lucy Llewellyn, book designer for and founder of Head & Heart Book Design who immediately 'got' the fable, indeed put all of her head and heart into the fable project. No Name and Bear and Witch and Fish and Bird, even King and Queen, all join to thank her from the bottom of their invisible hearts for her devotion to the work of fine designing and organising their existence on the page.

ABOUT THE AUTHOR

Guislaine Vincent de Damas, a nom de plume, has two lives. One – while waiting for the magic of a sentence and the secret alchemy of literature to happen – when she writes, sculpts, draws, and plays with her grandchildren. And one where she works as analytical psychotherapist (Jungian) with a private practice in Central London. She says this fable wrote itself. In this book she writes of her wish that its enticing and healing effect acts on the reader as it did on herself. *No Name* is Guislaine's first published not-quite-fairy-tale. Three more are to follow.

The author can be contacted by post… preferably handwritten… at Worlds End Studios, 132 Lots Road, London SW10 0RJ.

Oil portrait of Guislaine Vincent de Damas by Consuelo Child-Villiers

About the Illustrator

Consuelo Child-Villiers is a long established artist who free falls into a world of her own. No net. Independent. Thus her work is quietly widely collected in Europe and North America. Figures and creatures and objects and their secrets dwell in her vision which is both playful and serious. Consuelo's medium of expression is colour, colour as material fact, communication and soul-song in paint, usually and mostly oil paint. Consuelo studied at the Accademia di Belle Arti in Florence, Italy. Her mother-ground is centuries-old rooted in Spain, Mexico and Italy. Her father-spirit is Irish English. This is her second work in illustration working with watercolour.

www.consuelochildvilliers.com